Tales from tl

TALES FROM
THE VEDAS AND
UPANISHADS

RETOLD BY
Daaji
KAMLESH PATEL

Illustrated by Gayatri Pachpande

RED PANDA

RED PANDA

First published by Red Panda, an imprint of Westland Publications
Private Limited, in 2021

1st Floor, A Block, East Wing, Plot No. 40, SP Infocity, Dr MGR Salai,
Perungudi, Kandanchavadi, Chennai 600096

Westland, the Westland logo, Red Panda and the Red Panda logo are the
trademarks of Westland Publications Private Limited, or its affiliates.

Copyright © Heartfulness Education Trust, 2021

ISBN: 9789391234096

10 9 8 7 6 5 4 3 2

◈ Contents ◈

◆ Introduction ◆

Dear young friends,

We all love stories!

Today, you have access to millions of stories through books, TV, tablets, laptops and more—all at just the flick of a page or click of a button. Things were different when I was a child. I loved reading and hearing stories too. But stories for me, and for many before me, were tales from epics like the Ramayana, Mahabharata, Vedas and Upanishads.

These magical tales of gods and demons, warriors and wise people, of the timid and brave, of good and evil, completely captivated me. I often drifted off to sleep with thousands of questions in my mind, but knowing that all was right in my little world. At that time, these were just stories I enjoyed.

When we're young, our world is small. It's about our family, teachers, friends and our surroundings. As we grow up, we begin to understand that the world is much larger. I also realised that the stories from the epics I'd heard and read as a child weren't 'just' stories; they were a universe of learning. These tales are a part of a far greater tale, with lessons and learnings from life that span thousands of years.

Most of you are familiar with stories from the Ramayana and Mahabharata. This book you're holding in your hand shines a light on the Vedas and Upanishads.

The Vedas are important scriptures. They're considered to be teachings for human beings, told through sages, initially through the oral tradition of mantras, which form the oldest part of the

Vedas. Originally, students memorised the Vedas. There are four Vedas—Rig Veda, Sam Veda, Yajur Veda and the Atharva Veda. Did you know, some refer to the Mahabharata as the fifth Veda?

Upanishads are a part of the Vedas. The word *Upanishad* is made of three Sanskrit roots: *upa* (near), *ni* and *shad* (sitting down). It means to sit down near, and signifies the action of sitting down at the feet of the teacher or the enlightened one for spiritual discussions.

It's believed there are more than 108 Upanishads. I have always been inspired by the Vedas and Upanishads. Every time I read them, new wisdom from our ancestors shines through. It's like the first experience of the Heartfulness meditation I had with my trainer. It was life-changing. I believe that the stories from the epics are in the same league.

There are several versions of the Upanishads, and a few stories have other sources as well. I trust you will take the essence and inspiration from these ancient stories rather than focus on historical details. Ultimately, all these tales serve to help us on our life's journey and evolution.

This book, with twenty-five fascinating tales from the Vedas and Upanishads, is an exciting adventure into the heart's ancient wisdom, which is already present in all of us. Every time you read these stories, I hope you grow in wisdom and humility, intelligence and creativity, kindness and nobility. The heart, after all, has its own intelligence, the intelligence of feeling instead of thinking.

This noble tradition includes great rishis like Vasishta, Vamadeva, Narada, Atri and Agastya, sages like Ashtavakra and gods like Indra, Agni, Varuna and Vayu who appear again and again, in early Vedas, later in the Upanishads, and yet later still in the epics like the Ramayana and Mahabharata, to inspire humanity forever.

In modern times, it's quite amazing how, besides entertainment, the stories in this book could even help us find answers to questions that often plague us—Was I right? How do I get out of a tricky situation? What can I do to make my friendless angry? They can provide solutions to everyday challenges—squabbles with friends, tussles with parents, peer pressure, exam stress, online game addiction, and so on. This is because solutions don't come from being at the same level as the problem. We have to raise our awareness, increase our cognizance, improve our judgement, and then when we observe, the solution arrives through the simplest route.

For example, discovering these solutions is like solving a traffic jam on the highway by examining the situation from a helicopter. The police force aboard the helicopter can then give directions to the ground force to remove the blockage. In this collection of stories from the Vedas and Upanishads, we see that, in the midst of the greatest difficulties, mentors and gurus always guided their disciples to look for solutions from within the heart. Throughout time, the heart has always been held as the place of knowledge, the seat of wisdom, and the fount of love.

So let's read these lovely tales from the Vedas and the Upanishads. Just enjoy them or, additionally, pause to think about the essence of each story. At the end, what you draw from each story is your personal learning.

It is a very unique tradition and treasure trove. Enjoy!

—Daaji

1.

When the Gods Partied

The battle was fought between the mightiest. The gods, known as devas, and the demons, called asuras, clashed like never before. It looked like the evil asuras were about to win when Lord Indra, the king of the devas, prayed to the Supreme Being, called Brahman. Lord Indra had not seen the Supreme Being until then, but his teacher had told him that it was Brahman who created people. He made the sun rise, the plants grow, the birds chirp. It was also Brahman who decided the outcome of battles.

Lord Indra meditated upon Brahman to invoke him. As he explained the situation, his confidence grew, and he led the devas to victory.

How do you view challenges? How do you get the confidence to face your challenges?

With joy and pride, they celebrated. They drank and ate and made merry since their natural tendency is to enjoy.

However, in their merriment and pleasure, they forgot to thank the very Supreme Being who guided them to victory.

How do you feel when you are successful? Proud? Joyful? Both?

The celebration carried on to the next day, when suddenly, a huge, bright figure appeared at a distance. The devas were puzzled at the appearance of this unknown entity amidst their wonderful celebration.

'Who is this?' they asked each other. But they were too scared to approach the figure directly.

'O Agni! You are the god of fire! Could you please go and find out who or what that thing is,' one of the devas requested.

Agni agreed and approached the figure. As he came closer, the brightness was blinding, and he could not make out what the figure looked like. Before he could say anything, the figure spoke.

'Who are you?'

'I am Agni, the god of fire!'

'And what special power do you have?'

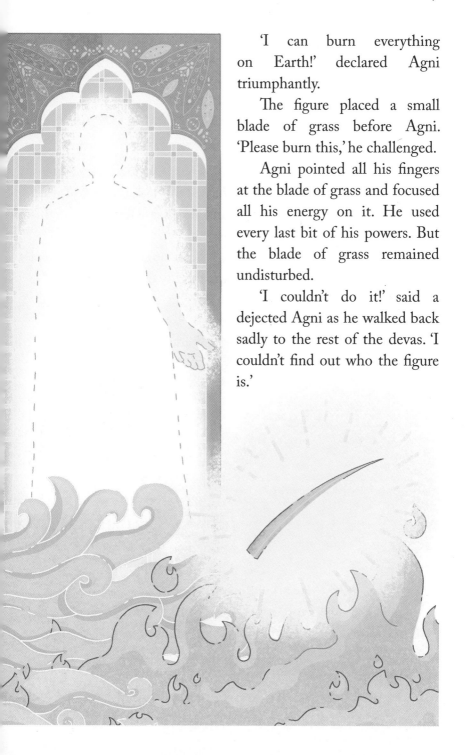

'I can burn everything on Earth!' declared Agni triumphantly.

The figure placed a small blade of grass before Agni. 'Please burn this,' he challenged.

Agni pointed all his fingers at the blade of grass and focused all his energy on it. He used every last bit of his powers. But the blade of grass remained undisturbed.

'I couldn't do it!' said a dejected Agni as he walked back sadly to the rest of the devas. 'I couldn't find out who the figure is.'

What is power? Who is more powerful—the big and boastful person, or the quiet one who does good for others with their power?

The perplexed devas now turned to Vayu, the lord of wind and air. 'Please find out who this is.'

Vayu agreed and approached the mighty entity.

'Who are you?' the figure asked.

'I am Vayu!'

'And what special power do you have?'

'I can lift everything on Earth with just my breath!'

The figure placed a small blade of grass before Vayu. 'Lift this meagre blade, please.'

Vayu rushed to the blade of grass with all his strength and blew with all his might. But the blade of grass did not move even a tiny bit!

Vayu, too, hung his head in shame and walked back to the other devas. 'I couldn't find out who the figure is.'

Finally, the devas approached their king, Indra, and asked him for help.

'Don't worry. I will find out who this is,' declared Indra, and set off to meet him.

Indra strode powerfully and purposely towards him, but the figure disappeared before his eyes. Indra was shocked and frightened. He knew this was a strange being. He decided to sit down, pray and meditate, as he had done earlier, to find a solution.

While he was in deep meditation, the Divine Mother suddenly appeared. 'Did you not recognise him, O King of the gods?' she asked. That was Brahman, the Ultimate or Absolute, himself!

'He is the Supreme One, and it is because of him that the devas won the great battle yesterday!' she said.

On hearing this, Indra immediately understood. He bowed his head and sought forgiveness from Brahman. All the other devas followed. 'Please forgive our false vanity and pride,' they said. ' We are indebted to you.'

'Do not worry,' Brahman said. 'Your understanding is all I need!' Then he blessed them all.

LET'S TALK ABOUT IT!

Isn't it fascinating how we often forget that we are only a tool of nature, but we start believing, 'I am doing it'. Perhaps if we forget the 'I' and the 'me', the action may happen naturally.

So how do we forget the lower self, the weaknesses of body, mind and intellect? Personally, I have experienced that by praying to the infinite power and connecting through the heart, we forget that 'I' am doing it, and thereby what needs to get done is done. Unfortunately, the ego comes back in and takes the credit for a job well done. But if you ponder over it for a minute, you realise that it is the forgetfulness of ego, the absence of egoism, that made the performance possible.

By transcending the relationship with the ego, by refining it, by becoming more and more humble, your consciousness can expand infinitely.

2.

The Dazzling Bird
on the Tree

Once, a great master asked his students, 'What or who awaits you at the end of the spiritual journey?'

Everyone had an answer.

One said, 'God.'

Another said, 'Oh, but there is no god. It is my spiritual teacher.'

So they went, on and on, about this and that in a philosophical way.

The master finally said, 'Let me tell you all a story.'

'Once, two birds were sitting on a tall tree with beautiful pink flowers and pretty, juicy, golden fruit. The birds' feathers were bright and beautiful—pink and yellow, blue and red, gold and silver in vivid arrays. One bird sat on the highest branch and the other on the lowest. The bird on the lowest branch ate the fruit of the tree. Some of the fruits were bitter and some

were sweet. Day after day, the bird on the bottom branch would look at the bird on the top and think, "How I wish I were so happy

How do you respond when you feel happy or when you feel sad?

and carefree like that bird! It is more beautiful and peaceful than I am!" But when the juicy fruits caught its eye, it forgot the bird above, and started eating the fruits.

'Alas! The bird on the lower branch would take one bite and cringe. The fruit was bitter and he would spit it out. He was unhappy. He looked up and saw the bird on the highest branch.

'Then he'd bite yet another fruit. This one was delicious, so he was happy. Again, he looked up and saw the bird on the highest branch.

'Interestingly, the bird on the highest branch didn't bite into any fruit—neither the sweet nor bitter ones. He just sat there calmly and serenely, majestic and glorious, happy to be who he was.

"'Oh, how nice it would be if I could meet that bird," thought the little bird on the lower branch with admiration.

What qualities do you think your highest self has?

'But then, he continued eating the fruits, going from a bitter bite that he would spit out to a sweet bite that he would relish. After a while, he got tired of eating these fruits and so decided to approach the bird on the higher branch.

'He began to fly up. But the branches hindered him. Some were sharp and scratched him painfully. He struggled for a while and hopped here and there, flying up and down. Finally, he made it to the topmost branch after a lot of difficulty. The bright rays of the sun enveloped him. We cannot be sure if the brightness was because of the sun or if he became bright from within.

'And do you want to know the surprising part now?

'There was no other bird on the branch!

What can you do so that you can become your higher self?

'The bird who had flown from the bottom branch had transformed into the bird sitting on the branch. He suddenly realised that there had been only one bird on the tree. The bird on the bottom branch had been merely a reflection of the bird who was on the top branch.'

Thus, concluding the story, the master said, 'Now tell me, what is awaiting you at the end of your spiritual journey?'

The students were silent for a long time, and finally, they understood—the beloved waiting for us at the end of our spiritual journey is our transformed self.

In reality, we are one with our highest self, but seeing ourselves as reflections makes us feel different.

LET'S TALK ABOUT IT!

Some of you may have watched movies like Marvel's *Endgame*, or read books with time travel as the central theme. Characters arrive in the past or the future, meet their younger or older selves to prevent a disaster, initiate a new evolutionary change, and go back to the present to witness the effect of that change. This, of course, is fiction. Now, look at the reality as we go deeper into the story of the birds. Our interest in a better and happier future version of ourselves is the moving force behind evolution, isn't it? It's like athletes who see a mental vision of themselves getting the Olympic Gold, when they put themselves through a gruelling but satisfying regimen of practice and diet, day after day, till they get there.

A firm will and undivided attention on what you seek is required. Everything that you seek shall then be found quite close to you—in fact, you yourself are that which you seek.

3.

What Did the Thunder Say?

Long ago, the devas, asuras and humans lived together in the universe. The humans, who lived on Earth, worked hard, farmed their land, built houses and lived with purpose. They gave birth, lived and died, which formed the foundation of everything they did on earth.

The devas lived in the heavens. They enjoyed their life, had a lot of food and entertainment and spent all their time in merriment. They lived for as long as they wanted, without any diseases or worries.

The demons or asuras were selfish and cruel. They insulted everyone and harmed and caused injury to the humans and the devas. They lived in the lower worlds.

Is there someone you could forgive today? Think of a person who has irritated or insulted you, and in your heart, bless that person and tell yourself that you have forgiven them. How does this make you feel?

This is the story of these three groups who decided to meditate together. They prayed to the Supreme, who created all of them. 'We want to improve ourselves,' they said. 'We want to be happy. We want to be respected and loved. Please tell us, O God, what should we do? Please teach us.'

And isn't this what we all want too?

'*DA-DA-DA!*'

There was a thunderous roar from the heavens. The same word repeated three times—*DA-DA-DA*—so sharp and clear. The devas, the humans and the demons heard it distinctly. Each group was convinced that the message was for them.

Now, you must be wondering what DA-DA-DA means. But guess what? Those guys knew, in their hearts, what the sound meant for their group. However, strangely, they arrived at three different meanings.

Humans thought that DA stood for *datta*, which means charity or to give. Generally, humans desire more of everything, are greedy, and want to be the best, even among their own brothers and sisters. So when they heard DA, they understood that to be happy they needed the generosity of spirit. They started sharing and helping each other out.

The devas understood DA as *damyata*, meaning self-control. So they decided to be moderate. They exercised self-control while having fun. They still enjoyed life but only in moderation. For example, we know that sweets are tasty, but too much can make us diabetic or sick. Playing with friends is good, but too much of it makes us neglect our studies or work. In the same way, devas had their own responsibilities, too. For example, Vayu was the custodian of wind, and Agni was the custodian of fire.

The third group, the cruel asuras, understood DA as *dayadwam*, or showing compassion, kindness and empathy. Since their nature was to hurt people, they thought that the creator had advised them to be kind-hearted.

The story ends here. But what about us, the people of today?

There is a human side, a divine side and a demonic side in all of us.

The DA-DA-DA from the creator helps us control ourselves by following all three guidelines in our lives.

The human part can help you become generous and willing to share with others without expecting anything in return. See how this transforms your life. The divine aspect needs to practise moderation and self-control. Too much pleasure can lead to it becoming an addiction. Last, demonic behaviour, which makes us want to hurt people or be revengeful, needs to go.

Sharing and caring are necessary even if you are wealthy. Moderation and self-restraint are necessary to be happy even if you are all-powerful. Forgiveness and compassion are needed to enjoy peace and co-existence even if you feel hurt. All three attitudes are required for balance and stability in individuals, society, and the whole world. This balance is what builds our character and keeps us growing.

LET'S TALK ABOUT IT!

Did you realise why the three groups interpreted the message differently? They all heard the same word repeated three times, didn't they?

That's because their inner needs were different.

The silent self, inside each one of us, is wise, and it knows subconsciously what we need to be taught. We all are unique in our need for correcting certain behaviours and attitudes. When we crave betterment, nature speaks through somcone, and our heart interprets it into the language we need for our benefit. The real teacher is inside, and the outer teacher comes only to reveal the real teacher within our hearts.

Share your resources.
Simplify your life to be in tune with nature.
Instead of revenge, feel the spirit of forgiveness
and compassion.

4.

The Cart Puller and the King

King Janashruti took care of all the people in his kingdom. He was kind and generous. He provided his subjects with food, wealth and every amenity they needed. He also built many rest houses for travellers and visitors from other kingdoms. He wanted them to have a good time, and he did not charge them any money. Generous, isn't it?

And this was something he was aware of. He often thought of how charitable and giving he was. He considered himself to be a great man.

King Janashruti knew the language of animals. One evening, as the king was enjoying the sunset in his palace garden, he overheard two swans conversing.

Are you aware of the joy of giving? Do you give freely to your friends? How do you feel after giving?

One said, 'Do you know, our king is the greatest of all? He gives so much to everyone. He is so charitable.'

The other swan replied, 'But the king is not greater than the cart puller Raikva. Raikva is a better person as he remains anonymous. The king is desperately pursuing fame.'

Hearing this, the king became restless. Imagine a great king hearing that there is someone better and greater than he is. King Janashruti was both curious and worried.

'I must find this little cart driver. Who could be this man who doesn't want to be famous, even though he gives so much?' the king murmured to himself.

He sent a search party into the kingdom. Finally, they found a man sitting under his cart. 'Are you Raikva?' asked the king's guards.

'Yes,' replied Raikva.

'We need to take you to the palace on the king's orders.'

Raikva shrugged and said, 'I'm not interested in meeting the king.'

When the soldiers reported back to the king, he decided to go and meet Raikva himself. He went with six hundred cows, gold ornaments, a horse-driven chariot and many other gifts to win over the cart puller and ask him to impart wisdom to him. But Raikva coolly said, 'I do not need these gifts. Please take them back.'

Who is the greatest giver you know? Your mother? Your father? Your friend? Why do you think they give freely?

King Janashruti went back dejected. The next day, he returned with more expensive gifts like diamonds and emeralds, and hundreds of servants.

But Raikva said, 'I do not need any of this.'

'I want to learn from you,' insisted the king; however, it fell on deaf ears.

Finally, Janashruti went back with his daughter and offered to give her hand in marriage to Raikva, a mere cart puller. Raikva was neither tempted nor amused by all this. But he was impressed by Janashruti's perseverance and dedication to learning, and this is an important quality for a good student.

Eventually, Raikva accepted the king as a student. On the first day of the king's training, Raikva said, 'We worship many elements. For instance, we worship the wind because it blows everything away. We worship fire because it can burn everything. We worship breath because it keeps us alive. But one important thing is that the human spirit's presence gives meaning to these elements. It creates and sustains the universe.'

The next day, Raikva said, 'To be proud of the charities we do is harmful. This pride will not truly help the receiver. Nor will it do anything for the giver. Give, but without ego. Give, not because

what you offer is yours to give. Give, because the divine spirit has given you what you have to share with others.'

Thus, many weeks passed and the king completed his learning with Raikva. He had finally understood the essence of giving. He gave Raikva all the gifts he had earlier brought with him, arranged the cart puller's wedding with his daughter, and left. This time Raikva accepted the king's gifts, as they were given without pride.

LET'S TALK ABOUT IT!

When we give with love, we think of the joy the receiver gets. This gives us joy. Being known as the giver does not give the pure joy that we get by giving anonymously. Another great thing is to give in such a way that the receiver feels that our joy in giving is more than their joy in receiving. When a mother feeds her son or daughter, she is happier than the child. The child doesn't realise that it is receiving from the mother. This is the way nature intends giving and receiving to be.

If you have a loving heart, give quietly. When you serve, serve with anonymity.

5.

The Boy Who Saved His Guru Crops

Aruni was one of the most outstanding students of Guru Dhaumya. Once there was a breach in the water channel nearby that irrigated the fields. This was dangerous for the crops, as a sudden gush of water could destroy them.

'Hurry, Aruni, check the water channel and close the breach,' instructed Dhaumya.

Aruni rushed to the fields, but the water channel was already broken. He tried to fix it. But even after working the whole day, he couldn't repair it completely. By this time, the sun had set and he was all alone.

What do you think of obedience? Should we always do what our elders tell us to? Or should we use our mind and make decisions for ourselves?

In those days, if your teacher told you to do something, you made sure to do precisely that. So Aruni wasn't about to disobey his guru. He wondered how to fulfil his teacher's orders.

After thinking a lot, he found a solution. He lay down on the field just across the breach and plugged his body into the channel. This stopped the water from flowing out into the crops and damaging them.

The crops were, of course, saved. The night wore on and then the morning dawned. Aruni continued to lie in the same position, unmoving, plugging the breach.

'Where is Aruni?' asked Dhaumya the next day in class.

'You had sent him to fix the breach in the water channel yesterday,' replied one of his students. 'I haven't seen him since then.'

'Let's go to the field and search for him,' Dhaumya said, worried.

Dhaumya and all his students searched the fields for Aruni. But nobody spotted him. Finally, Dhaumya began calling out in a loud voice, 'Aruni, where are you?'

Hearing his teacher's voice, Aruni called out feebly, as he had not eaten or slept for a whole night and a day. 'I am here, blocking

the water channel from flooding the fields.'

Dhaumya and his students hurried to the source of the voice and found Aruni lying down, plugging the breach.

Do you think there is more than one way to solve a problem? Think of an example and discuss it with your friends.

'I cannot get up,' Aruni said. 'If I do, the water will flood everything. I couldn't find any other means to fix the channel.

Dhaumya was naturally overwhelmed by Aruni's devotion. The boy had braved the bitter cold night lying in the water, with just two thin pieces of cloth around him.

'Oh, brave and compassionate Aruni!' Dhaumya said. 'Your devotion is the greatest. By this one act of sincerity, all the Brahma Vidya will shine deep within you.'

In those days, the relationship between a teacher and a student was extraordinary. It was marked by service and sacrifice, love and devotion and humility and honour.

LET'S TALK ABOUT IT!

Whether you are a student or a teacher, a son or daughter, or anyone else, perseverance is an essential ingredient for success and joy in school or elsewhere. Basically, perseverance is when someone continues working towards an objective regardless of the difficulties or delays in achieving it.

We all know life is full of struggles, and it is easiest to give up when faced with adversity. Like Aruni, those who persevere use their minds and bodies to overcome it. He set a goal for himself and worked hard for it.

Serve, but without the feeling that it is low.
Think of serving in that way as an honour and
a privilege.

6.

Is It Smart To Be Humble?

Long before Yagnavalkya became a great teacher, he was a student of Guru Vaisampayana. As a young boy, Yagnavalkya was very gifted and used to assist his teacher in holy errands.

The king of the land once invited Vaisampayana to his court and asked him to conduct a ritual in the palace to bless everyone.

'Oh, but I have already committed to other rituals on that date,' Vaisampayana said. 'Can I send my student in my place?'.

The king gladly agreed as he did not want to offend the guru.

'Dear Yagnavalkya, please go to the palace and conduct the rituals to make the king happy,' Vaisampayana requested.

Yagnavalkya conducted the ritual and wanted to give the

Have you had the unexpected pleasure of learning something great from a very young person?

prasad, or holy offerings, to the king. It was believed that this sacred offering had the blessings of God. But the king had already left. Yagnavalkya waited for a long time, but the king never returned.

Meanwhile, the king had assumed that a senior assistant of the guru would offer the prasad at a later stage. He did not expect Yagnavalkya, a mere boy, to offer the prasad. When the king did not turn up to receive the offering, Yagnavalkya got angry. He dumped the prasad on a dead log and walked away in a huff.

After a few days, the king was surprised to see leaves, branches and beautiful flowers sprouting from the dead log. 'This log has been dead for decades! How strange that new leaves are sprouting.'

The queen replied, 'Do you remember that young boy Yagnavalkya? He conducted a ritual here on behalf of his guru. Well, he poured the prasad on this tree. The new leaves are sprouting because of his *sankalpa* and blessing: "May this family grow; may this family prosper."'

'I should have stayed to accept his prasad,' brooded the king.

So the following year, the

How do you process feelings like anger, sadness or disappointment?

king again decided to conduct the same ritual and went to Vaisampayana's gurukul. 'Please could you send young Yagnavalkya to my palace to carry out the same ritual?'

If you were in Yagnavalkya's place, what would you have asked for from the Sun God?

'Of course,' Vaisampayana said. 'He shall be there at the appointed time.' Vaisampayana replied.

Unfortunately, things panned out differently. Yagnavalkya was in no mood to go to the palace that year. 'Sir,' he said to his guru, 'last time the king insulted you. He went away before I could offer him the prasad. So I do not want to go to the palace this time.'

Yagnavalkya was a young boy, and his immaturity was the reason for his irritation and anger. His guru gently tried to appease him. 'Perhaps the king made a mistake. Why don't you forgive him?'

'No,' Yagnavalkya said, firmly. 'Let us not throw pearls before swine.'

Vaisampayana grew angry. 'This arrogance is not good for you, my dear boy,' he said. 'If you do not want to obey me, then you have to return all the knowledge that I have given you and leave.'

Reluctantly, Yagnavalkya 'vomited' all his knowledge and left with a heavy heart. Yes, it was possible to 'vomit' or return the knowledge you had acquired in those days! They had all sorts of abilities. When this happened, Guru Vaisampayana asked a few of his other disciples to become partridge birds (called thithri in Sanskrit) and swallow this knowledge, as knowledge can never be wasted. Those birds then became humans again and passed on their knowledge, which came to be called the Taittiriya Upanishad, part of the Krishna Yajur Veda, an ancient text all about rituals.

Meanwhile, what happened to Yagnavalkya? He meditated and invoked the Sun God. The Sun God was pleased by his meditation and said, 'What do you want, my dear?'

'Please give me that which would make you happy, and that which would make the world a happy, peaceful and safe place,' Yagnavalkya replied.

Yagnavalkya's attitude, mind and heart had evolved into something pure, without arrogance. That is how he received knowledge from the Sun God, which has come to be known as Brihadaranyaka Upanishad and is part of the Shukla Yajurveda.

LET'S TALK ABOUT IT!

Both the king and Yagyavalkya learnt that humility serves us well. The more humility we have, the more we can evolve. My spiritual teacher, Ram Chandra of Shahjahanpur, used to say, 'There is nothing wrong in thinking ourselves to be great, as long as we think others are greater.'

There is a hidden benefit in this way of thinking too. It always allows us to look out for the good in others. When we think of how they are better than we are, it lends a natural opportunity for us to learn the best from all of those around us. This is the first step towards evolution in a fundamental sense. It's because to evolve means to become better than before.

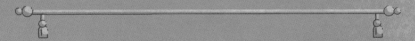

The more humility we have, the more we can evolve.

7.

The Perfect Recipe for Miracles

Uttanka was a student of Guru Gautama. He served him not for five or ten or twenty years, but a cool hundred years. Can you believe that? Guru Gautama adored him so much that he did not let him go, even after his education was over. Uttanka grew old and weak and now had grey hair.

One day Uttanka collapsed under the weight of a huge bundle of firewood. Gautama's compassionate daughter cried at the sight of the old man struggling to carry a pile of wood.

Uttanka felt bad for upsetting his guru's daughter. So he asked Gautama, with tears in his eyes, 'Why have you not let me go home even though my education

Do you have a favourite teacher? Why is that teacher your favourite?

is over? Thousands of students have enrolled, studied and left. Yet here I have been for more than a hundred years.'

On hearing this, Guru Gautama restored Uttanka's youth through his spiritual powers. He arranged for Uttanka to marry his daughter. After the ceremony he said, 'You may leave now. Go and have a wonderful life with my daughter.'

'What guru dakshina can I give you?' asked Uttanka. In those days, students gave a gift to their teacher before departing from the gurukul.

'I want nothing from you. I am pleased with you. You have become what I wanted you to become. That is my guru dakshina,' he said. But Uttanka insisted on giving Gautama something. The guru reluctantly said, 'You could ask my wife, your guru-mata.'

Gautama's wife had a strange request. 'I want the divine earrings of Madayanti, who is the wife of King Mitrasaha Saudasa.'

Unfortunately, King Mitrasaha Saudasa had been cursed to be a cannibal and he wanted to eat Uttanka. Uttanka approached

What would you do to make your teachers happy?

him and explained, 'It is my duty to get Madayanti's earrings as guru dakshina for my guru-mata. After I deliver them to her, I shall come back and offer myself to you as a sacrifice.'

The king agreed. 'Go then. Hurry! Get Madayanti's earrings. She is in the palace.' Uttanka asked for the king's friendship which he granted. He then asked the king to advise him about a serious matter with total honesty and truthfulness as a real friend. The king agreed. Uttanka asked him, 'If you were in my place, would you come back and agree to be killed? Is it not a duty to protect one's own life?' The king was trapped by his own promise and told Uttanka to go away and not come back. Uttanka thus cleverly escaped being killed.

Now, Madayanti refused to part with her earrings. 'How do I know that you are who you say you are and that my husband has given his consent for me to give you my earrings? Go back to the forest and bring a token from him.' Uttanka went back to the forest and returned with a ring from the king. This time, the queen willingly parted with her earrings.

'Be careful with them. The nagas or snakes, the gods, the demons—they are all waiting to steal my earrings. So never let these earrings touch the ground,' she warned.

Uttanka tied the earrings in deerskin and kept the pouch safely hidden under his clothes. While travelling back to the ashram, he became hungry. So he stopped to pluck some fruits and eat them. While doing so, the deerskin kept getting in the way, so he tied it to the branch of a tree. But it fell and the earrings rolled out onto the ground.

A snake saw the earrings spill, immediately took them, and rushed into an anthill. Uttanka was dismayed. He dug into the anthill for thirty-five days, but it was so deep that he still didn't get to the bottom of it. Indra, the king of the devas, saw Uttanka digging as he drove past on his chariot. He offered his weapon, the famous and powerful Vajra, and using this, Uttanka entered the kingdom of the snakes, Nagalok.

There, Uttanka saw a horse with a black-and-white tail. Its muzzle was copper coloured and its eyes shone with splendour. The horse was the god of fire, Agni, whom Uttanka worshipped in his ashram, and who had come there to help Uttanka. The horse told him, 'Blow air on me, from behind me, and see what happens!' Uttanka obeyed him, and immediately flames erupted and engulfed Nagalok with fire and smoke.

With all the fire and smoke, the snakes began to choke. Vasuki, the king of the snakes, came out of his abode and begged for forgiveness, returning the earrings to Uttanka. Uttanka happily forgave him and quickly made his way to his guru's home to offer the earrings to his guru-mata.

Uttanka was delighted that he had fulfilled his guru's wish of making his wife happy.

LET'S TALK ABOUT IT!

There are many times in our lives when we serve with joy, wanting to be part of the bigger plan. You must have helped out in family weddings, birthday parties of family or friends, or even neighbourhood projects. You helped without expectations and with the desire to contribute and be part of the joy. What if we lived our whole lives with this joy and zest? Then our everyday tasks and duties may have a different flavour while we dispense them. When joy, love and passion are added to voluntary service, the service becomes valuable.

When love is present, the idea of duty vanishes.
The idea of work vanishes. When we love, we
fulfil our duties in the most natural way, without
ever feeling their burden.

8.

Weighty Issues

The guru Ayoda Dhaumya called out to one of his students, Upamanyu, 'Go and look after the cattle.' Upamanyu immediately obeyed. From that day onwards, he would wake up early in the morning, tend to the cows, watch them graze until evening and then bring them back to his guru's ashram.

One such evening, after Upamanyu returned, Dhaumya said, 'You have put on some weight. This may not be good for your health. What do you eat every day?'

Upamanyu answered, 'Master, I support myself with alms.'

Dhaumya replied, 'A student should always offer the alms to his guru first, before consuming them himself.'

Has anyone ever given you any advice for your improvement? How did you accept it? Write down how you felt in your journal.

So Upamanyu offered the alms to his guru, but Dhaumya did not share them. Are you surprised? Upamanyu was not; he did not complain. Instead, he tended to his cattle as his guru had instructed earlier. Days, weeks and months passed.

'Son, I take all your alms. But you are still plump. What and how do you eat?' replied Dhaumya asked one evening.

'After I give my alms to you, I go seeking alms again,' Upamanyu said.

Dhaumya was amused, but he hid it and instead chastised the young lad. 'That is not fair. The other people who seek alms will be denied their share if you do this. Do not do this again.'

Of course, our little lad Upamanyu obeyed his guru again.

After a few days, Dhaumya asked again, 'I am sure you have stopped begging for alms a second time. And yet, you have not lost weight. How do you nourish your body?'

Upamanyu replied, 'I drink the cows' milk.'

'That isn't right. The cows' milk is for their calves,' the guru said.

Upamanyu acknowledged his words and stopped drinking milk from the cows.

Yet again, in a few days, Dhaumya asked, 'My dear child, you no longer eat from the alms you receive, nor drink milk from the cows, and yet you have not lost weight. What do you eat these days?'

'When the calves suckle from their mother, their faces are covered with froth. I lick that froth, and that is enough for me.'

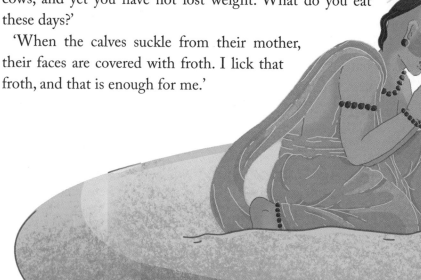

'This also is unjust, dear son. The calves sense your hunger, and so they leave behind a lot of froth for you. Please refrain from doing this.' Now Upamanyu was hungry. He saw no option but to eat some leaves

Do you keep your promises? To your elders, to your parents, to your teachers? Why? How does this make you feel?

and berries from the forest. But a few of the wild berries turned out to be poisonous. The young boy became blind and fell into a well.

After the sunset, Dhaumya saw that Upamanyu had not yet returned home. He became worried and set out in search of his student. He called out many times and finally heard Upamanyu's voice from inside the well.

'I fell into the well because I became blind,' said Upamanyu.

'Meditate and pray to the Ashwini Kumaras,' Dhaumya replied. 'They are the twin physicians of the gods in heaven. They will restore your sight.'

Upamanyu did as his guru instructed.

The twins were invoked. 'Drink this potion,' they said. 'Your eyesight will be restored.'

Upamanyu refused it, saying, 'Please offer it to my guru first. I have promised not to eat anything without first offering it to him.'

To play a prank, the twins said, 'Once, when we offered the same potion to your guru, he drank it without offering it to *his* guru. So why bother? You can just drink it.'

But our little boy was not to be tempted even with the promise of eyesight. 'My vow to my guru is final,' he said.

Finally, the Ashwini Kumaras were delighted with Upamanyu's devotion to his guru, and they restored his vision. They also blessed him to be prosperous and happy.

Dhaumya was thrilled with his student for passing all tests he had set for him, and said, 'You shall obtain all the prosperity the Ashwini Kumaras have blessed you with. Moreover, all the knowledge of Brahman will illuminate your heart.'

LET'S TALK ABOUT IT!

I often ask those who come to me to use their heart when they come with a problem. I say, 'Do not expect too much.' Life is all about acceptance. Whether it is a situation, business ventures, or a partner, it is acceptance that makes them all successful. Can we say, it is the same in the case of a teacher too?

Even a bacteria or virus mutates to survive in a hostile atmosphere, so, why can't we? We have to learn to constantly accept, which can then help us adapt to situations, without being disturbed. This acceptance will help us flourish, thrive, and perhaps find great joy. My teacher often used the term 'cheerful acceptance'. If we think about it, there is so much wisdom in the term.

Joys and sorrows are vibrations in opposite directions. Our attitude changes everything. Once we have enough conviction in ourselves to achieve our goals, disturbances here and there don't actually matter.

9.

The Boy Who Met the Lord of Death

Nachiketas was the son of Vajasravas, a great learned man. Once, Vajasravas performed a ritual known as Viswajeet Yajna. According to the ritual, he was supposed to give away his wealth and cows in exchange for a boon from God.

Now the hero of our story, Nachiketas, observed that his father gave away only old and wrinkled cows that could not be milked anymore. 'Father,' he said, 'these cows are of no use to us, and by giving them away, we are not sacrificing them. So why are you doing so? Aren't you supposed to give away good and healthy cows as a sacrifice?'

Vajasravas did not reply. Nachiketas again asked him the same thing. Vajasravas again did not reply.

If you were granted three boons, what would you ask for?

Now Nachiketas was really unhappy. He was a very pure soul. So he repeated his question to his father in a louder voice.

Why do you think Nachiketas was not tempted by Yama's gifts and insisted on knowing the secret of death?

When you question your parents again and again, what happens? They get annoyed, right? That happened here too.

Vajasravas replied angrily, 'I will give you away as a sacrifice to Yama, the god of death. Will that make you happy?'

'Oh sure, father! I am happy to go and meet the Lord of death.'

'Then so be it,' Vajasravas said.

Nachiketas cheerfully left for the realm of the dead to meet Lord Yama. But Yama was out to carry out his official duty of collecting great souls at the time of their death. So Nachiketas waited at the gates for three days and three nights. He was hungry and thirsty, but he waited patiently.

When Yama returned, he found Nachiketas at his doorstep and was amused by the young boy's perseverance. He offered him some water and said, 'Dear Nachiketas, you waited for me for three days and three nights. So let me offer you three boons. Tell me what would you like?'

Nachiketas replied, 'For my first boon I want my father's anger to be dissipated. When I go back to Earth, may he

welcome me with open arms, and may he always be loving and kind and compassionate towards me.'

'That's one easy boon, my dear son. Granted! What is your second boon?'

'Let me learn all the steps to make sacrifices to the gods. I want to be virtuous and serve the gods in the best way possible.'

'I shall teach you everything you need to know about this,' said Yama, and went on to teach Nachiketas all the rituals and codes of conduct.

'For my third and final boon, O Lord, teach me the secret of life beyond death,' said Nachiketas.

'My dear son, please ask for any other boon instead. I shall give you the greatest treasures of the world. I shall offer you fertile lands, a hundred healthy and smart children instead,' replied Yama.

'But after I enjoy all that, one day when I die, would I not meet you again?'

'Yes, indeed!'

'And then I would again ask you the same question. So please tell me now, what is the secret of life after death?' asked Nachiketas.

Very happily, Yama shared the secrets of life, death and the beyond. 'When we die, our body perishes. But the real self inside does not die. It is called the soul. The soul is immortal. The soul is smaller than the smallest and bigger than the biggest. 'Our body is like a chariot. Our intelligence is the driver, the sense organs are the horse, and our mind makes up the reins. The soul is the master or owner of the chariot. That soul is superior to the sense organs, our intelligence and even our conscience.

'Now, even greater than this individual soul is the enveloping super consciousness, which is the seed of the universe. Greater than the universe is the ultimate, or Brahman. Our goal in this life is to be one with that supreme self or God.

'"Arise, awake, stop not till the goal is reached," say the wise sages, "because the path to realisation is sharp and narrow like a razor's edge and difficult to walk on. One has to overcome many weaknesses like laziness, temptations and desires. It requires sincere work, purity, alertness, and most of all, humility."'

'Thank you, dearest Lord,' Nachiketas replied. He then returned to the open arms of his father and went on to live a great life, helping many others in this pursuit.

LET'S TALK ABOUT IT!

The greatest lesson you can learn from Nachiketas is the value of focus. Regardless of the temptation, do not lose your focus, your discrimination, your wisdom, or aim. Success goes to the person who is focussed. As Bruce Lee once said, 'The successful warrior is the average man, with laser-like focus'. Your success depends on your focus.

Let me share a secret with you all about focus—focus comes to a rested mind and a pure heart. Whenever I use the Heartfulness Relaxation, I feel my mind relaxing. A relaxed mind focuses better. I urge you to try it, whenever you have the need to focus. For example, just before preparing for an exam, or even for a few minutes in the examination hall before you start writing your exam, and so on. A pure and clean heart has better reasoning, which is also very essential in our everyday life.

The more a human being can tell the difference between right and wrong, the cleaner their soul.

10.

Who is the Best?

'I am the best!' declared the eyes. 'Without me, you cannot see anything in this world.'

'Oh, but that's not true!' shrieked the ears. 'Without me, you would hear nothing. You wouldn't respond to anything and would look foolish.'

The senses of our body began fiercely fighting about which one was most important.

Finally, they all decided to stop arguing. They asked the creator, 'Who is the best among us?'

The creator replied, 'If a sense organ leaves the body and the body still functions, that is fine. But if a sense organ leaves the body and the body collapses, then isn't that the most important one?'

So one by one, each sense organ decided to leave the human body for a year. The tongue was the first to go. When it returned, it asked the others eagerly, 'How was life without me?'

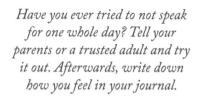

Have you ever tried to not speak for one whole day? Tell your parents or a trusted adult and try it out. Afterwards, write down how you feel in your journal.

The other organs replied, 'We lived like a mute person. We did not speak to anyone. But we breathed with the prana, we saw with the eyes, we heard with the ears, and we thought with the mind. It was uncomfortable, but we survived.'

Now, the eyes departed from the body for a year. When they returned, they asked the other organs, 'How did you live without me?'

The other organs responded, 'We lived like a blind person. We did not see anything. But we breathed with the prana, we spoke with the tongue, we heard with the ears and we thought with the mind. We are still alive, as you can see.'

Then it was the ears' turn to leave the body. When they returned after a year, they asked, 'Life must have been terrible without me, right?'

Try the Heartfulness deep relaxation (given at the end of the book) and write down how you feel in your journal.

But the other organs just laughed and said, 'We lived like a deaf person. We did not hear anything. But we breathed with the prana, we spoke with the tongue, we saw with the eyes and we thought with the mind. We managed well enough.'

Then the mind left for a year. When it returned, it asked the same question: 'So, did you miss me?'

'We lived like one whose mind is not yet formed. We were not able to think. People thought we were so stupid. But we breathed with the prana, we spoke with the tongue, we saw with the eyes and we heard with the ears. So we survived.'

Finally, it was the prana's turn. The breath of life decided to go away for a year too.

What do you think happened? When the prana was about to depart, the whole body reacted violently, shivered and almost collapsed. All the organs shouted together, 'Wait! Don't leave us! You are the most important one! We cannot live without you. The entire body will die without you.'

'Oh, Prana,' they said, 'we have life only because you exist in the body. We realise you are life itself. We are merely the expressions of life.'

That is why great importance is given to pranayama, which includes simple breathing exercises for health. Good breathing helps maintain good health.

LET'S TALK ABOUT IT!

The breath of a person is essential because it is the life force. Keep observing your breathing patterns at various times and try to infer what it means.

Do you know that breathing exercises like pranayama give you better lung capacity? They increase your immunity and your ability to survive better in high mountains and even cities with air pollution. Better and deeper breathing, improves oxygen supply to the brain and aids brain function too.

Here is a different benefit of breathing exercises, which you may not know. When you feel yourself getting angry or stressed, close the right nostril with your thumb, and take a slow deep breath through your left nostril. Breathe deeply into your abdomen and release the breath fully each time. Continue this eight to ten times through the left nostril.

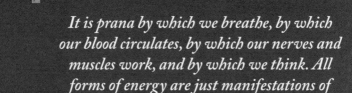

It is prana by which we breathe, by which our blood circulates, by which our nerves and muscles work, and by which we think. All forms of energy are just manifestations of prana.

11.

How To Focus Best?

Do you know the story of Satyakaam, the young fatherless boy who learnt from nature and later from Guru Gautama what Brahman is? Well, the young lad went on to become a great guru when he grew up and opened a huge gurukul. Many students enrolled under him and became wise in their own way.

This is the story of Upakosala, one of Satyakaam's students. It so happened that Satyakaam did not allow him to leave the gurukul even after he had studied for twelve years. Satyakaam's wife pleaded with him to let Upakosala go back to his family and home, like the rest of the students, but Satyakaam was adamant.

How many desires or wishes do you have? What are they? Write them down in your journal.

To avoid further discussion, Satyakaam went off on a pilgrimage. Upakosala was sad because now he could not persuade his guru to let him go. He had to wait for his return. Once, Satyakaam's wife asked Upakosala to join them for the day's meal. He cried out in anguish, 'Mother, I cannot eat. I am miserable. My heart is filled with so many desires.'

Deep down in his heart, Upakosala knew that the problem was his attitude. His guru would let him go when he corrected his mindset.

Upakosala knew that though desires gave him sorrow, they were not good or bad. They just distracted him and did not allow him to perform his duties effectively. So Upakosala tried to remove his desires from his mind. But that is not an easy thing to do, is it?

One day, when he was tending to the ritual fires in the ashram, the fire spoke.

'Prana is Brahman,' it said. 'Joy and the sky are forms of God or Brahman too.'

Later, when he was inside the house, the household fire told him, 'The earth, the sun, fire and food are also different forms of God.'

Another fire said, 'Water, the directions—east, west, north and south—the moon and the stars are God too. This is the knowledge you need to hold— that all the elements are God. Your guru, Satyakaam, will guide you on the right path.'

Do you spend time in nature? Do you walk in the park, go swimming, or enjoy the rain? What is it about nature that makes you happy? Do you feel the presence of God when in nature?

On Satyakaam's return, he said, 'Upakosala! Your face shines! Did you learn what Brahman is?'

'Yes, the fires taught me,' the boy replied.

'What did they teach you?'

Upakosala explained what he had learnt. Satyakaam was thrilled to see that his attitude had improved. 'Let me teach you more.'

Thus began the disciple's journey of learning that the inner self is Brahman or God. Finally, Satyakaam declared that Upakosala had completed his education and was free to leave the gurukul.

LET'S TALK ABOUT IT!

When you have one overriding ambition, passion, or desire, you will
put your energies into it and achieve success. If you have a dozen
desires, your energies are frittered away. When a man was told to dig
a well to get water, he lost hope after digging ten feet at one place
because he did not find water. He started digging ten more holes,
of ten feet each, and found no water. When a great saint saw him,
he said, 'If you had dug a hundred feet in one place, you would have
found water'.

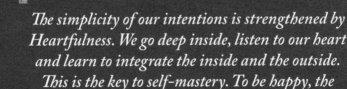

*The simplicity of our intentions is strengthened by
Heartfulness. We go deep inside, listen to our heart
and learn to integrate the inside and the outside.
This is the key to self-mastery. To be happy, the
inside and the outside need to be in harmony.*

12.

The Golden Mongoose and the Wonder Soup

Once, two great Vedic scholars sat down to eat lunch together. They topped their plates full of food, and when they were just about to scoop a spoonful into their mouths, a young boy entered the house unannounced and said, 'I am hungry. Can I have some food?'

The two scholars found themselves in an awkward situation. They looked at the boy with hesitation. The boy realised this and said, 'I am a Brahmachari. I follow Brahman or God.' Perhaps he was Brahman himself in the guise of a little boy. Just wait to hear what the boy told them next.

The young Brahmachari was not willing to take no for an answer. He continued confidently, 'God comes to us in

Would you share your meal with someone who needed it more?

many forms. We do not see God with physical eyes alone. Food is also a form of God. And when God comes to you in a physical form and asks you for food, are you going to say no?'

Have you had a friend share food with you when you were hungry? How did you feel about it?

The two wise men were ashamed, yet they remained silent and unmoving.

So the boy said, 'Let me tell you a story!'

Once upon a time, there was a starving family of four who sat down to have dinner. A hungry old traveller knocked on the door. Sensing that he was hungrier than any of them, the father of the family offered the man his bowl of soup. The old traveller finished it in one gulp and looked at them with hungry eyes. Seeing him still weak, the lady of the house offered him her bowl of soup too. He gobbled it up and was still hungry. The son offered his bowl too, and finally, the youngest daughter, a mere child, offered her bowl. The guest finished everyone's share of dinner and immediately turned into a bright light.

The guest was God in disguise. God said, 'I came to test you and show the whole world what true hospitality means. This incident will be etched in history and discussed again and again as the perfect example of hospitality.'

Then the Divine Being disappeared.

A small mongoose walked into the house and tried to lick the drops of soup that had fallen. It slipped and fell. Its body shone like gold wherever it touched the drops of soup.

Much later, this mongoose arrived at a feast offered by a rich king for the poor in the country. Seeing the mongoose roll over on the floor, again and again, the king became curious. He asked it, 'Why are you doing this?'

The mongoose said, 'Someone told me you are organising a feast for charity, so I came to see if my body will turn into gold by rolling over the leftover food. This had happened at the poor family's house long, long ago. I am sorry to see that it has not happened here. Therefore, this is no match to that family's charity.'

With their full plates of food in front of them, the two scholars looked at each other.

The boy continued, 'I am not asking you to sacrifice your food for me, like the poor family did. All I am asking is that you share it with me. You will also be saved from overeating and indigestion, or, even worse, the sin of throwing away your leftovers. Food is a gift from God, even if you have worked hard for it.'

The old men felt ashamed and shared their food with the young boy.

LET'S TALK ABOUT IT!

Another Upanishad enlightens, 'Let the knower of food never condemn food. Let them make food plentiful, grow food. Never deny lodgings to anyone. Never deny food to guests. Treat your mother, father, teacher and, most importantly, your guest as God!'
These values create a very hospitable and generous heart. We start by consciously doing these things, creating mental habits and thought patterns, and eventually, nobility becomes our DNA. I request you to instil these values consciously for a few weeks. Observe and note the changes you see in yourself.

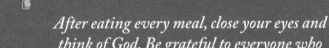

After eating every meal, close your eyes and think of God. Be grateful to everyone who made the meal possible.

13.

That 'Thing' Inside a Seed

Shvetaketu was the son of Uddalaka. Both of them were enlightened souls. The Upanishads speak so greatly about them.

When Shvetaketu was twelve years old, he was sent to study under a guru. He returned home when he was twenty-four years old.

'Father! I know all the Vedas, the rituals and shastras,' he announced. 'I have been educated in everything.'

Uddalaka detected conceit. He said, 'Shvetaketu, my dearest son, do you know anything about the unhearable, the unknowable, or the unperceivable?'

'What is that?' Shvetaketu asked.

His father replied, 'If you know the properties of a lump of clay, you can figure out the nature of all objects made of clay without necessarily knowing about every single object made of clay. So do you have that kind of knowledge, son?'

'Father, I do not. Please teach me,' Shvetaketu replied.

'Bring me a fruit of the fig tree,' Uddalaka said.

Shvetaketu brought a fig.

'Now break it,' Uddalaka said.

The young man broke it.

'What do you see?' Uddalaka asked.

'There are seeds.'

'Take a seed and break it open.'

With some difficulty, Shvetaketu broke the seed.

'What is inside?' Uddalaka asked.

'Nothing,' a surprised Shvetaketu replied.

'That nothingness has the subtlest of the subtlest essence that births this huge fig tree. That nothing is this whole tree.'

Shvetaketu was shocked and impressed. 'Tell me more, Father!'

'Pour salt in this earthen pot of water.'

Once this was done, Uddalaka said, 'Now, let's continue tomorrow morning, dear son.'

The next morning Uddalaka asked Shvetaketu to bring the pot of water with the salt.

Have you broken and prised open a seed? Have you looked at it under a microscope or through a magnifying lens? What did you find?

When Shvetaketu brought it, Uddalaka said, 'Remove the salt you poured inside.'

'But it has dissolved, Father.'

'Well, in that case, taste the water from the top of the pot.'

Shvetaketu took a tentative sip. 'Father, it is very salty.'

'Now take a sip from the middle and the bottom,' Uddalaka requested.

'Those are also salty,' Shvetaketu said.

Uddalaka now asked, 'Tell me, my son, have we lost the salt or have we not?'

The son answered, 'We have not lost it. It has dissolved in the pot of water.'

'In a similar way, your body contains your subtlest essence, and that is the real you.

'Tat Tvam Asi—thou art that. You are Brahman, the Supreme Being, and your pursuit to understand that, experience that, is the purpose of your life, dear son.'

Thus ends the beautiful experience between this father and son.

Which is your most precious relationship? Your mother? Father? Brother? Sister? Friend? Anyone else? Think about them and write in your journal why this relationship means a lot to you.

LET'S TALK ABOUT IT!

If we go by what we see, or hear, we may lose the real. Science tells us that even matter is mostly space between the electron clouds and nucleus, rather than the mass in neutrons. There is also greater space between galaxies than the matter in galaxies. Matter, too, is mostly congealed energy, or condensed vibrations. And the quantum world goes further beyond. Ernest Holmes said, 'God is all there is—God includes everything, all possibility and all action, for Spirit is the invisible essence and substance of all forms.'

Therefore, it is true that feelings, love, and joy are always more important than things that appear in front of our eyes. But, we have to give some importance to things because we live here in this world. The second important thing to notice in the story is the beautiful exchange between this father and son. Relationships like this are precious when knowledge is shared. And may we all be blessed to have such pure, noble, loving relationships in our lives, where we have the opportunity to understand Godly love through our loved ones. It is said, 'God is love.' Love is the first lesson of life, and the first teacher is the mother or father.

Spirituality is a sort of feeling or consciousness of the highest. It is the doorway through which to enter divinity.

14.

The Symphony of the Whole

There were once five students studying under a young guru in an ashram. He taught them the Vedas, scriptures, sciences, art and many other things.

One day, the five students asked him, 'Teach us how to connect with God.'

'That is possible only through meditation,' the guru replied. 'Why don't you all choose something you like a lot, something you think may be similar to God. Meditate upon it daily. You can then tell me how you feel.'

The first student meditated upon the sun. The second one meditated upon the moon. The third upon the infinite sky. The fourth upon the vast expanse of

68

water in front of him. And the fifth upon the earth. They all felt very peaceful and their minds were calm and clear.

However, they were unsure if this feeling was the connection to God they wanted. They spoke about their doubts and hesitations to their guru.

Have you ever put together a jigsaw puzzle? How does it feel to arrange different pieces of the puzzle to complete the picture? What does it indicate about life?

The teacher said, 'Come, let us see the king in the next city. He is known to be an enlightened person.'

When they met the king they asked him the same question. 'First, tell me how you meditate,' he said, 'then I will teach you what I know.'

Each student described his method to the king. The king listened patiently and then said, 'It has stopped raining, and the sun is shining. Come, let's go for a walk in the beautiful garden.'

On their stroll, he pointed out a majestic rainbow. 'How many colours do you see?'

'Seven,' a student said, 'violet indigo, blue, green, yellow, orange and red.'

'How many of these colours are needed to make the sun's white light?' the king asked.

'All the colours,' one of the students said. 'If even one is missing, the combination will not be white.'

'God is like that. He is included in all that you meditated upon and also all that you can ever meditate upon.'

Farther down the road, outside the garden, they saw a big elephant. The king asked them if they had heard the story of the four blind men trying to describe an elephant by touching it. 'Yes, of course!' they exclaimed.

The students continued excitedly, 'One blind man touched the leg and said the elephant was like a wide pillar. Another touched the ear of the elephant and said it was like a drum. Another felt the beautiful tusk and said the elephant was like a thick piece of bamboo. Yet another touched the tail and said it was like a rope.'

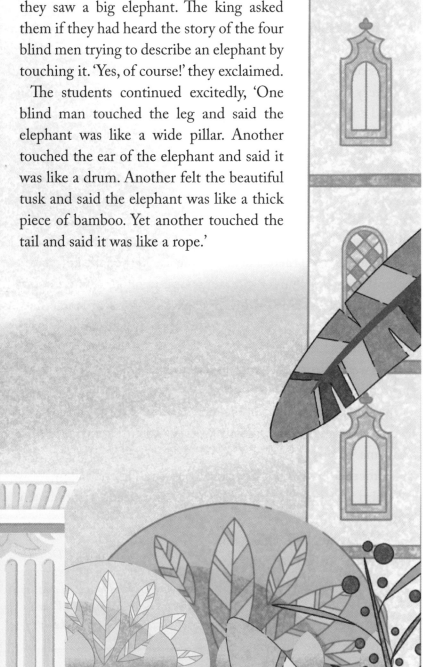

'So you see how difficult it is to know even the nature of an elephant by feeling only a part of it? Can the Supreme Being be less than that?' asked the king.

He sat down with the students. 'Meditating on the sky is good, but it is only the head of God; it is vast. The sun is like the eye of God, very bright. The moon is the same. Meditating on the wind is good too; it is like the breath of God. Water is also good; it shows you the fluidity of life. Earth is like the universal support of all things.

'The Supreme Being is all these, and everything else too. Anything you see or touch or feel is a part of that God. You yourself are a part of God. The entire universe is God.'

The king asked the students to join him for lunch at the palace.

The queen served them a delicious meal, and then the king asked them, 'When you finish your studies, you will go home to start a career as a teacher, a farmer, a warrior, an artist or something else. Will you want to make a new home, get married and make a home for your children?'

They were silent. The king asked them, 'Do you know what married life is like?'

One student said, 'I left home long ago, and I forgot what I saw. I know my parents were mostly worried about how to face life's problems.'

Another said, 'My parents were always smiling and happy.'

A third one said, 'There used to be tension and fights in my home all the time.'

The king laughed and said, 'Yes. All your experiences are true and part of all your families.

There is agony and joy, pain and pleasure, many opposites in life. To use these opposites in

What is your family like? Do they fight a lot? Or are they affectionate with each other? How soon do they make up after the fight? What do you do to ensure they make up?

the best way you can is wisdom. That only teaches you the fullness of life. Life is a school, family is a school, the world is a school that makes you realise the Supreme Being, God.'

Finally, he said, 'If a dirty and dishevelled person knocks on your door and says they are hungry, you give them the food you have. There, you have worshipped that Supreme Being who lives in their heart too! And you feel like you are one with the Supreme Being!'

LET'S TALK ABOUT IT!

Nothing makes God happier than teamwork and unity. Nothing makes God sadder than discord and friction. God is totality, completeness, oneness. And when we represent the same, we resonate more with that essence of godliness.

Diversity allows for creativity and evolution. When coloured threads in a fabric come together, the beauty of the fabric is seen. Like all the music instruments come together and play in their unique way in an orchestra. A garden has several flowers with different colors and fragrances. Though they are different, their combined presence gives joy. And that joy is akin to godliness.

A person who becomes one with all, who sees all in one, is always with God.

15.

Can Broken Promises Be Forgiven?

When Lord Indra learned that the great sages Nara and Narayana were in a deep meditative state in the forest, he became a bit worried. He did not want the sages to acquire more divine powers than he had, so he decided to distract them by sending apsaras.

Apsaras, as you perhaps know, were beautiful dancers in the court of Lord Indra. They sang and danced to entertain the devas. And now they danced gracefully in front of the sages. But Nara and Narayana remained unaffected by the dancers' charm. They were a bit irritated, and wanted to teach the apsaras a lesson. So Narayana created Urvashi, a stunning apsara, who was prettier than anyone they had ever seen. The other apsaras were a bit jealous of Urvashi's beauty and they left for Indra's abode, Devlok, in a huff.

Have you ever made a promise? Do you keep your promises?

Now, Nara and Narayana reassured Indra, 'Please don't

worry. We do not want to take over Devlok. In fact, you could even invite Urvashi to join you and be a part of your court. She could be the pride and beauty of Devlok.'

Have you ever felt that the promises you made or someone made to you have been silly?

Indra was very happy to have the beautiful apsara in his court. Thus Urvashi, the most beautiful apsara, stayed on in Devlok.

Many years later, Pururavas, the famous king of Prayag, performed a penance that pleased Lord Brahma. As a reward, he was made the king of the Earth. Pururavas met Urvashi in the land of Gandharvas, another celestial group of beings, where he fell in love with her.

'Would you marry me, beautiful apsara,' he asked Urvashi.

'Yes, I will, but I have three conditions,' she said.

'I shall fulfil them, whatever they are,' Pururavas readily agreed.

'The first condition is that I shall eat only certain foods,' Urvashi said. 'The second is that you should protect my pet sheep. And the second is that we should always be well clothed'.

'I agree,' Pururavas said. Both conditions seemed reasonable. And so Pururavas and Urvashi lived happily for some time.

However, Indra started missing Urvashi in his court. He missed her songs and dances though he was also aware of the three conditions of their marriage. He thought for a while and devised a way to get Urvashi back in his court.

'Let me send someone to steal Urvashi's pet sheep,' he thought.

When Urvashi found her sheep was missing, she was heartbroken.

'My sheep is missing! You have broken the first condition,' she cried to Pururavas.

On hearing her cries, Pururavas was distressed. He ran out to look for her sheep, without bothering to wear his clothes properly. And thus, the second condition was also broken.

On seeing that Pururavas broke her two conditions, Urvashi was heartbroken. She returned to Devlok. Pururavas was devastated too. A dialogue between Urvashi and her husband Pururavas is mentioned in the Rig Veda, where he requests Urvashi not to leave him. But she still does, because of the broken promises.

LET'S TALK ABOUT IT!

If you have ever made a promise, or someone broke a promise made to you, you already know how terrible it feels. You feel let down. Making a promise is like asking the other person to have faith in you. It's all about trust. When a promise is broken, the trust is broken, too, and breaking promises frequently can lead to mistrust. It's natural to feel sad when a promise is broken. But often, plans change or situations may force people to break promises they intended to keep. When certain things cannot be changed, it is better to accept them as they are.

Have you heard of the Serenity Prayer?

God, grant me the serenity to accept the things I cannot change,
Courage to change the things I can,
And wisdom to know the difference.
Trying to imbibe this in our life and lifestyle would do us good, to march
on towards success.

Anyone can change your destiny, but people
who are not egoistic, who are determined,
don't say, 'I have to keep my promise.' They do
what needs to be done at the moment.

16.

The Power of AUM

Have you ever played chess and arrived at a stalemate? The same thing happened once when the gods and the demons fought with each other. There was no result. So the gods decided to chant Udgita or the song of heaven. It's another name for the mystical sound AUM or Om.

The flow of creation started with the original vibration and is represented as the original sound—AUM. It has three parts—A, U, and M, which represent creation, preservation and dissolution. All three are present in AUM. AUM is in our innate memory within the soul. A represents the external wakeful state, U symbolises the inner dream state, and M stands for the deep sleep state.

Have you been interested in things only because you can see, hear, taste, or think? Or is there something that attracts you from the heart?

The gods meditated upon AUM and imagined it to be the breath inhaled through the nose. The demons pierced the nose easily with evil. The gods were defeated. Now the nose started smelling both good and foul odours.

The gods then meditated on AUM as speech, but the demons pierced it with evil. So we began to speak both truths and lies. The gods could not win by the purity of speech.

The gods now meditated upon AUM as hearing. But demons pierced it with evil again. Thus, we began to hear both good and bad things.

After that the gods meditated upon AUM as vision. The demons pierced this also with evil, and the capacity to see both good and evil was acquired.

Now the gods meditated upon the AUM as the mind. This was also pierced with evil by the demons. And the mind became capable of creating both good and bad thoughts.

Finally, the gods meditated upon AUM as the primary life force of the soul. The prana that sustains all life is free from likes and dislikes. So it could not be subdued by evil. When the demons tried to stab it, nothing happened. The gods won and they understood the significance of AUM and the soul.

Do you feel drawn towards things like a walk in the woods, a swim in the river, or a trek in the hills? Why do you feel drawn towards these?

LET'S TALK ABOUT IT!

Victory came to the gods when they thought of AUM as a symbol of the highest and identified it with the highest life force. It is the original vibration that led to the creation. As it is the purest, it is free from likes and dislikes. If we are attracted or repelled by things or persons, we cannot match that purity. Though our senses and minds can be corrupted with likes and dislikes, our original life force or the soul is always very pure.

AUM is the original sound at the time of creation. It is still there in memory within the soul. We transcend from A (wakeful state), U (dream like state), M (deep sleep state) to the stillness of silence.

17.

Meditate the Right Way

Balaki was a scholar of the Vedas. And he was proud of that! He wanted to show off his knowledge to the emperor of Kashi, Ajatashatru. So Balaki went to the court and said, 'O King, I shall teach you all about Brahman or God.'

The king was genuinely happy. He received Balaki with respect and said, 'Generally, all scholars rush to King Janaka to teach him because he is spiritually advanced. It is kind of you to come and teach me.'

Flattered, Balaki said, 'Let me begin by teaching you how to meditate. I shall teach you to meditate on the sun as I do.'

King Ajatashatru humbly replied, 'The sun is not absolute.

Think of a time you felt you did way better at something than you expected to. How do you think you did that? Write it down in your journal.

The reality behind the sun is the resplendent light. I meditate on the light. This light could take many other forms, so ultimately we do not focus on the object of the light, which is the sun, but the essence of the light.'

Balaki was surprised by the reply, but continued, 'I also meditate on the moon. I shall teach you to meditate on the moon. The moon is also Brahman.'

When you learn new skills, how do you find ways and means to put them to use?

The king replied, 'I meditate on the moon too,' the king said, 'but it is slightly different. The moon is huge and glows, and gives immense delight. So I meditate on the abundance and eternal quality of the moon, and not the moon itself.'

Balaki now said, 'I meditate on the flash of lightning, as that is Brahman too.'

'Dear Balaki,' the king said. 'I meditate on lightning, but not the way you think. I meditate on its radiance. There are other forms of radiance too. A person who meditates on this brilliance also becomes brilliant.'

Thus continued the dialogue between Balaki and King Ajatashatru. Balaki continued to explain how to meditate on the sky, wind, air, water, earth, body and shadow. Every time King Ajatashatru explained how one needs to meditate on the essence of something, and not on the object itself.

At last, Balaki silently waited. King Ajatashatru said, 'We cannot know the absolute by meditating on an object alone.'

'Would you take me as your student?' Balaki asked, at last. The teacher now wanted to be taught.

But King Ajatashatru did not show any arrogance. He felt happy to share whatever he knew with Balaki. He held Balaki's hand in his own, and the two went for a walk.

King Ajatashatru taught Balaki about Brahman. They spent many days together, and the king gently changed Balaki's limited belief system.

Once when they were walking through the city, they saw a man sleeping. The king called out his name, but the man didn't react. But when the king shook him awake and mentioned his name, the man responded. The king said to Balaki, 'When he was awake, he knew I was calling his name. When he was asleep, he was not aware that I called his name and he could not respond. Now, where did that consciousness go during sleep? And from where did it return when he woke?'

Balaki didn't know the answer.

So the king answered, 'This consciousness absorbs the functions of the senses, like hearing and seeing. It rests in the space inside the heart. When this consciousness is active, it extends throughout the body, and that was when he was awake. Therefore, when he was awake his consciousness was in his ears also, and he heard our call.'

Then King Ajatashatru helped Balaki go into a meditative state and understand the essence of life. Slowly Balaki realised that the same essence was in him too, and became one with it.

In our schoolbooks, we have learnt the story of the lion's cub who grew up among a herd of sheep right from its birth. As a result, it thinks of itself as a sheep. But when a grown lion meets it, takes it to a lake, and shows the cub its reflection in the water, self-realisation dawns on the cub naturally, and it roars like a lion.

Those who goes deepest into meditation are similar. They realise they are Brahman in essence.

Balaki was extremely grateful for this experience with King Ajatashatru. He returned as a humble man after learning to meditate with the king.

LET'S TALK ABOUT IT!

What we conclude with this story is that appearance doesn't matter as much as the essence. Balaki had to learn that the essence matters more than the appearance. When the sleeping man appeared to have lost the consciousness of his name, it is still hidden in the memory inside his heart. And when he came to waking consciousness, he could recognise that it was his name.

In our perception, we evolve from thinking to feeling. From feeling into being, being into becoming, and finally, beyond.

18.

The Mystery Behind True Knowledge

'Can you teach me the highest truth?' Narada asked Sage Sanatkumara.

You must be wondering how the truth can be high or low. But Sanatkumara had an interesting way of explaining this to Narada.

'I will teach you beyond what you already know,' he said. 'Tell me, what did you study?'

'I know the four Vedas and the epics,' Narada said. 'I have studied science, grammar, mathematics, astronomy, philosophy, psychology and fine arts'.

Have you ever tried to meditate? Close your eyes and focus on the light in your heart. Can you feel it? After five minutes, open your eyes and write down whatever comes to your mind about your awareness and what you felt. Start with the practice of heartfulness relaxation, given in this book, and see if it helps.

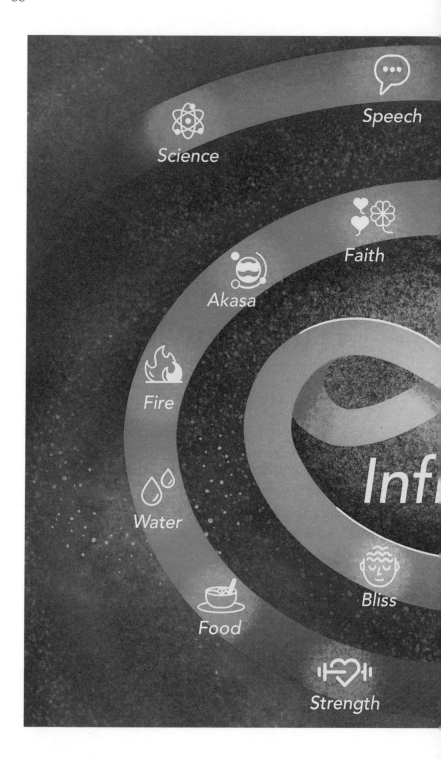

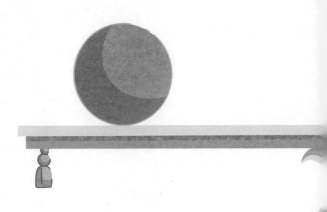

'Oh, but these are all just words. Do you know what is greater than these?' When Narada didn't reply, Sanatkumara said, 'Speech is greater than words because it is by speaking with each other that we communicate the knowledge of sciences and arts.'

Those were the days when they didn't write things down but memorised everything, so speech was essential.

'Is there something greater than speech?' Narada asked.

'The mind is greater than speech,' Sanatkumara said. 'We think using the mind. When we think, we use our willpower. Willpower is greater than the mind. But consciousness is greater than the will.' So the mind must be clear, the will must be strong, and the consciousness must expand.

How can you become great here on Earth? By becoming rich? By buying loads of cars and houses? By getting more followers on social media? By becoming a CEO? Or by being remembered with love and gratitude?

'That's a big word consciousness. What does it mean?' Narada asked.

'Consciousness means to be aware of oneself and one's environment,' Sanatkumara said. 'This awareness is unique to every individual.

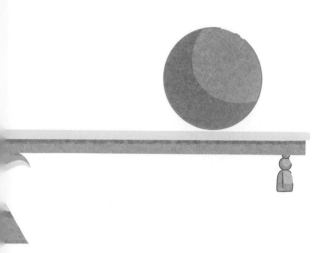

However, it is more than the immediate too. Meditation is greater than consciousness, because it is meditation that expands our consciousness. And that gives us awareness and then understanding.'

'So understanding is the greatest!' Narada announced triumphantly.

Sanatkumara smiled. 'Understanding is not enough. If you do not act on it, what use is it to you? You need inner strength to act on your understanding! Therefore, strength is greater than understanding.'

'Okay, what gives us strength?' Narada asked.

'Food gives us strength, and water is necessary to produce food. Water comes from rain, which is produced by fire or the heat of the sun. The sun's heat evaporates water from the oceans and the lakes and forms rain-laden clouds that pour rain. Fire or heat lives in space or akasa. Akasa exists in the mind of man, which is dependent on hope and faith,' said Sanatkumara.

'Something tells me that is not the end of it,' Narada said.

'Not yet. Hope and faith are dependent on life, or prana, and that depends on truth,' said Sanatkumara.

'Thank you!' Narada said. 'That was my initial question, and finally, I have my answer.'

'But there is more. Don't you want to listen to it?' Sanatkumara asked.

'What can be greater than truth?' asked Narada.

'By using the power of reflection, we understand the truth. This is possible by single-mindedness. If you complete your duties towards your family and society, you will have a single-minded approach. Otherwise, you will be worried about them. After performing your familial and other duties correctly, you can reflect on absolute truth with single-mindedness. That will give you bliss, or ananda.

'This bliss can be found only in infinity,' Sanatkumara said. 'Measurable things cannot give us bliss. Man must know infinity.'

'Wow! What is infinity?' Narada asked. 'How can I find it?'.

'Everything on Earth is finite. It depends on one thing or another. But the infinite is independent of everything. It is more than you can think of or measure. Interestingly, the infinite can be perceived in one's own inner self. Sages have experienced that the inner world is vaster than the outer one, and it is easier to reach the unlimited therein rather than the outside. So by going inside the heart and meditating, we can experience it. For that, let us purify the mind and regulate the senses. To purify the mind, remove negative thoughts. Regulate the senses by not overindulging and by being moderate. Then when we sit silently and observe the inner heart prayerfully, we will not merely know the highest truth but be truth ourselves.'

This is how Sanatkumara taught Narada to meditate on the light in his heart to know his inner self.

What have you done so far, to be remembered with love and gratitude?

LET'S TALK ABOUT IT!

Thinking about the secret behind true knowledge can lead to many ideas, depending on our situation or need. But the best way forward will always be through simplicity and purity, through a silent, clear and clutter-free mind. Meditation can help give us a fresh perspective.

Do you remember the story of Lord Ganesha, who circled his parents, proclaiming them to be his whole world, instead of racing around the world like his brother? The brothers were competing in a race to travel around the earth fastest for a reward—a juicy fruit.

Simplicity can solve problems in the best way. Look within the heart first!

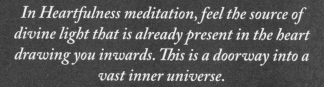

In Heartfulness meditation, feel the source of divine light that is already present in the heart drawing you inwards. This is a doorway into a vast inner universe.

19.
The World Beyond

Have you ever heard of home schooling? Well, in the olden days, there was a smart young man, Shvetaketu, who was the son of Uddalaka Aruni, a renowned sage. He first studied in an ashram far away from home but returned to study with his father. Uddalaka was the greatest of the gurus, so, after being homeschooled by his father, Shvetaketu considered himself smarter than everyone.

One day, Shvetaketu decided to show off his intelligence to the ruler of the land, King Pravahana. When he reached the court, King Pravahana asked, 'Have you completed your education?'

'Of course, I have,' Shvetaketu said. 'Ask me anything, and I shall answer.'

'Do you know where all living beings go after death?'
Shvetaketu was taken aback. 'No, sir, I do not know.'
'Do you know how they return to earth?' the king asked.
'I do not know that either.'

'Do you know about the two paths—the path of light and the path of darkness—along which the dead travel?'

'I do not know, sir,' Shvetaketu said, embarrassed now.

'Do you know why the land of the dead does not become full, even though so many people die every day?'

Alas, he did not know!

'Well then, let me ask you something else. Do you know how the elements of the earth come together to become a living person?'

Shvetaketu's jaw dropped. He just stood there.

'My dear friend, your education has not even begun.' Though the king's response was kind, he dismissed the young man.

Shvetaketu felt awful. He went home and asked his father, 'Why did you not teach me the basics about life and death and the world beyond?'

Uddalaka listened to all that had happened in the palace and said, 'I do not know the answers to any of these questions. Let me go and ask King Pravahana himself.'

The king received Uddalaka with great respect and said, 'I offer you immense wealth to improve your gurukul. This will benefit all your students.'

'Please tell me the answers to the questions that you asked my son,' Uddalaka asked. 'That would be a greater service to all my students.'

Though King Pravahana was happy that Uddalaka was interested in learning about the world beyond the ashram, he was also in a fix. 'Sir, traditionally this knowledge has been received only with warriors, and it has never left our clan. But for the first time, a scholar like you is seeking this from a warrior like me.

Do you think about your life on earth? Do you believe in afterlife?

'Elemental matter gets converted into life by going through five stages. These five stages represent five sacrifices. In the first stage, the matter is sacrificed to the fire and the sun. Thus, life-giving sap is

What do you think makes a person cruel? What makes them compassionate?

produced. In the second stage, this sap is offered to the rain god, Parjanya. When rain falls on the earth, food is produced—this is the third stage. When we consume food and digest it, a vital fluid is produced, and this is the fourth stage. This vital fluid is different for men than for women, and in the fifth stage, this fluid is united to form a child, which is a new life. This is how elemental matter becomes a life-giving force.'

The king continued, 'Now let me tell you the secrets of the soul and other worlds. After our lifetime, our body disintegrates into earth, water, fire, ether and air. But the soul is always alive. What happens to the soul depends on how we lived as humans. If we live a life in remembrance of God, we will go on the path of light and reach God. If we live a life of honesty and virtue, we will be in heaven for a short period and then

return to Earth. However, if we committed crimes and were cruel, we will be forced to go through a lot of suffering in life-and-death cycles. This is why the land of the dead is never full, because all who die do not reach there.

'So be thoughtful about how you spend your time on Earth, as that makes you reach God through the path of light.'

Uddalaka thanked King Pravahana with all his heart for this deep spiritual knowledge, then he returned to his school to teach what he'd learned to his students.

LET'S TALK ABOUT IT!

We need to be prepared for the many transitions or changes in this life. Have you ever seen a tearful child who doesn't want to leave her parents and face the teacher in kindergarten? She needs to accept the change cheerfully and get ready for this new phase. Then comes progress and growth. That takes time and habit.

In higher classes, there are new admissions every year, but is the school ever full? No, because children move on to the next class and the class then receives the next batch of students.

Take the case of a bright student who learnt all lessons well but loves the teacher of this class so much that he doesn't want to go to the next higher class. 'She's affectionate to me. How can I be without her?' he asks. Would you not call him a fool? Life has to move, and so do we, so that we're not left behind. How we spend time in each class in school, determines our promotion to the next stage. Life goes on. There's no fixed end, only stages we pass through!

To be ready for the next stage of life, it is better to remain in a state of love, peace, and joy. This creates a lifestyle where we are prepared.

20.

Understanding God

Varuna was the god of the oceans and water, and a great sage was named after him. This sage had a son named Bhrigu. One day, Bhrigu asked him, 'Father, can you please teach me the secret of understanding God.'

'You can seek that by meditating, dear son.'

'What do I meditate upon?'

'You will figure it out, Son,' Varuna said.

'Give me a hint, Father.

'Well, our sense organs are the prana, eyes, ears, mind and speech. They all need food to survive. Begin your introspection there, from food.'

Bhrigu followed his father's words and meditated. He finally

concluded that food is God. 'We are born from food, and we eat food to live. So food is God,' he said to his father.

'Yes, dear Bhrigu. But Brahman is more. Continue meditating, and you will know more.'

After many days of meditation, Bhrigu went back to his father. 'Prana, or breath, is God. We are born because we breathe. And after we die, we return to air.'

'Yes, you're right, but continue meditating, dear son. Let's see if there is more,' replied Varuna.

After a long meditation session, Bhrigu excitedly reported back, 'Father, the mind is God. We are all born because of the mind. We live because we think.'

'Indeed, son, you are absolutely right. But meditate more,' Varuna said.

Bhrigu was excited with that reply because he knew that he was only going to learn more. After months and months of meditation, Bhrigu went back to his father with a lot of joy and said, 'Knowledge, or *Vignanam*, is from where all of us are born. We live because of our wisdom, and we return to it.'

'Son, I appreciate your wisdom in finding this. However, do

Try meditating on objects like Bhrigu did. For example, meditating on objects/aspects in nature, such as the sun or the moon, the trees, wind or water, is a good idea. Write down how you feel about each of these in your journal.

Now try to meditate on the light in your heart for ten minutes every morning. Write down your experiences in your journal.

meditate one last time, and let us see what we discover.'

Bhrigu wasn't at all disappointed. With a lot of confidence, he went deep into his meditation. He experienced great bliss, or anandam.

When Varuna came to know about his son's realisation, he was thrilled. This time he greeted Bhrigu with joy. 'Dearest son, this bliss is the highest form of existence. Now there is no need to teach you more.'

LET'S TALK ABOUT IT!

The story ends here saying bliss is the Brahman, or ultimate God. But one can go beyond that to feel one's soul and even God. Even in everyday life, can we always be blissful? If we eat the tastiest food every day, are we not fed up or bored after a while? Remember the story of the gods who were always enjoying themselves, and the thunder said, 'DA, DA, DA', and they realised too much of good is also bad. Life always needs a balance. And to find that balance, we need to go beyond the coverings.

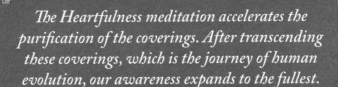

The Heartfulness meditation accelerates the purification of the coverings. After transcending these coverings, which is the journey of human evolution, our awareness expands to the fullest.

21.

What Can Nature Teach You?

Satyakaam's mother worked as a domestic aide in many houses. The boy aspired to learn Brahma Vidya, which is the ultimate knowledge. So he went to Sage Gautama's ashram and said, 'Sir, I am Satyakaam. Would you please accept me as your student?'

'What is your father's name?' Guru Gautama asked. 'What is your family's name?'

Now Satyakaam didn't know his father's name, or his family's name. So he ran back to ask his mother. She said, 'I do not know, my dear son. But you can tell Guru Gautama that you are Satyakaam, son of Jabala, the housemaid. Always be brave and tell the truth.'

When he approached the sage and told him the truth, Gautama was stunned.

Have you spoken the truth even when it was difficult to do so? How did that feel?

'I don't know if this boy comes from a respectable family,' he thought. 'But what honesty for such a young heart! And what eagerness to study! I am lucky to enrol him as my student.' Thus started a beautiful journey between the teacher and the student.

Soon Gautama realised that Satyakaam was far ahead of all his other disciples. He felt that nature could directly teach him. So the sage selected four hundred cows and bulls. 'Gautama,' he said, 'take them to the forest to graze. Return to the gurukul only when they grow to be a thousand.' A gurukul is the home of the guru, where the student lives and learns.

Have you taken walks in the woods with your parents or family members? Have you hugged a tree? How does it feel to be one with nature?

Satyakaam happily accepted his guru's orders and took care of the cows in the forest for several years. Since the forest had a lot of green pastures and healthy foliage, they grazed well and grew healthy. Satyakaam had no distractions in the forest, and so he meditated a lot.

One day, a bull said, 'Now our numbers have grown to a thousand. Shall we return home to Guru Gautama?'

'Of course! But let me ask you a question before that. Do you know what Brahman is?' Satyakaam asked tentatively.

'There are four quarters of Brahman, each representing a quarter of the universe. Brahman manifests in the four directions—north, south, east and west. The four directions are equally illuminated, and so by meditating on this, one becomes enlightened. The fire will teach you the next part of Brahman.'

Satyakaam thanked the bull.

In the evening, Satyakaam kindled the fire, and the fire said, 'The second quarter of Brahman is the earth, sky, heaven and ocean. Meditate on this and you will realise that Brahman is infinite. It is beyond any end.'

Have you learnt anything from nature? What and from whom?

'Thank you, but what are the other two quarters of Brahman?' Satyakaam asked.

'You will receive that knowledge from the swan,' said the fire.

The next morning, Satyakaam saw a beautiful swan swim towards him. It declared, 'The third quarter of Brahman consists of fire, sun, moon and lightning. One who meditates on these understands that Brahman is light.' Then the swan swam away.

Later in the day, a sunbird flew towards Satyakaam 'Are you ready for the fourth and final lesson?' it asked.

'Yes, indeed,' exclaimed Satyakaam with great reverence.

'The final quarter of Brahman is experience itself. Brahman manifests itself in prana, the eyes, the ears, and the mind. Your ability to understand the world around you is Brahman. Now you are ready to go back to your gurukul.'

When Satyakaam reached his gurukul, Gautama saw his radiant face and immediately exclaimed, 'You now know Brahman!'

'Yes, sir, the bull, the fire, the swan and the sunbird taught me the four quarters of Brahman. But I'm still missing something. It is only you who can teach me that,' Satyakaam said.

'You already know all that is to be known. There is nothing that I can teach you,' insisted Guru Gautama.

'Sir, I may have the knowledge of Brahman, but only you, my guru, can give me the experience of Brahman.'

'Then come, let's meditate together, and learn this, my son. Brahman is inside you, in your heart, which is full of love for God.' And so they meditated.

LET'S TALK ABOUT IT!

'Nature is our Teacher. She unfolds her treasures to our search, unseals our eyes, illuminates our minds, and purifies our hearts. An influence breathes from all the sights and sounds of her existence,' said Alfred Nobel.

The forests are not a luxury or a privilege, but a necessity. They're as vital to our lives as water and food. Looking at the deforestation happening every day, I wonder if we're giving the gift of forests to our children, grandchildren, and their grandchildren.

A planet that destroys its vegetation, destroys itself. Forests are the lungs of the Earth, purifying the air and giving strength to our people. Let us not kill our great teachers, because our lives depend on their lives .

I urge you all to consider this matter seriously—plant as much as possible. Not for you or me, but for the future of our species' survival, which depends on this. I also observed that these places naturally aid in sustaining a deeper spiritual meditative practice.

Trees, plants, earth and water, tell us that places endowed with the bounties of nature have greater power of transmission, increased capacity for protecting the truth and for longer durations. Such places attract and influence people's feelings and provide an ideal atmosphere for a spiritual practice.

22.

Can You See in the Dark?

Once upon a time, there was a great king called Janaka. He knew all about castles and kingdoms, people and politics, wealth and wisdom. His kingdom greatly prospered under his rule.

But he wanted to learn more about the intangible wealth that wise men always speak of. One day, he announced that he would donate a thousand cows with gold tied to their horns to the best Vedic scholar in his kingdom. He wished to learn deeper spiritual truths from such a person.

Many wise scholars and sages arrived at the palace to participate. Alongside them, came a sage called Yagnavalkya, who immediately declared that he should receive the thousand cows. The other scholars were offended. They thought that Yagnavalkya was arrogant, and so they put forth a long list of difficult questions. But he answered all to their satisfaction.

Have you tried asking your heart what direction to go in when you are facing a challenge?

Finally, a great woman sage called Gargi asked him, 'What is above the heavens, below the earth, and in between

Yagnavalkya answered, 'Akasa or space.'

'What is present in space?'

'Brahman or God,' Yagnavalkya said, 'God is everywhere, and in space too.'

Upon hearing this, King Janaka enthusiastically accepted Yagnavalkya as his teacher. Yagnavalkya taught him many things and shared deeper spiritual truths.

Once Janaka asked him, 'What serves as a light to guide us?'

'The sun!' Yagnavalkya said. 'Its rays are deeply nourishing.'

'And when the sun has set?'

'The moon,' the sage answered.

'And when the moon has set?'

'Fire,' Yagnavalkya said.

'And when the fire goes out?' Janaka asked.

'Speech!'

'And when speech has stopped?'

'The light within the heart,' Yagnavalkya concluded.

Then, looking deeply into the king's eyes, Yagnavalkya said gently but firmly, 'And now, let me teach you to meditate and find that light in your heart.' Then they both closed their eyes and meditated together on the source of light and love in the heart.

After teaching the great King Janaka how to meditate, Yagnavalkya returned home to his ashram with the thousand cows. King Janaka was grateful to the sage for having shown him the experience of true inner courage, freedom and light through meditation.

Yagnavalkya continued to teach and learn, and everyone around him benefited. However, after a long while, and after fulfilling all his duties, he wished to go to the forest and meditate for a long time. So he told Maitreyi, his wife, 'I want to go to the forest and meditate. Would you like to have half of my wealth? I can give the other half to Katyayani.' She was his other wife.

'Dear husband,' Maitreyi said, 'will it make me immortal if I receive all this wealth?'

'No. One day, you will die too.'

'In that case, I don't want this wealth. I want only that which would make me immortal.'

'That is an interesting request,' Yagnavalkya said. 'Let me teach you something!

'A wife loves her husband, not for his sake but for her own. Parents love their children for their own sakes too. Thinkers and teachers are also loved for the sake of their own selves. Warriors and kings are loved for the sake of their selves too. The gods, our beautiful Earth and everything living on it are loved not because

of who or what they are, but for the sake of one's own self. It is important, therefore, to realise this great self within you.'

'Dear husband, what is this self?' Maitreyi asked. 'Is it me, myself?'

'Yes and no. You can only experience this higher self in your own heart when you rise up above the lower self.'

'But what is the higher self?' Maitrey asked. 'And what do you mean by the lower self?'

'The lower self is that which seeks pleasures, avoids pain, falls into the cycle of rebirth and gets trapped in worldly pursuits. The higher self is something I can enable you to experience. Let me teach you to meditate.'

So Yagnavalkya taught Maitreyi to meditate on the source of light in the heart. Maitreyi had chosen the path of real knowledge and wisdom rather than that of material possessions and wealth.

Whom do you love the most in the world? And why?

LET'S TALK ABOUT IT!

When the heart is clear, so is the mind. When the heart is at peace, the mind is at rest. So, for any problem solving, we start with the heart and integrate it with the mind. When we integrate the heart and mind while trying to find ideas or solutions, we do so with unbridled joy.

Listen to the heart carefully. Follow it faithfully. Let it be your inner compass.

23.

Striking a Balance

The period of Rig Veda is known for a few famous husband-wife teams of sages. One such team was Rishi Vasishta and his wife, Arundathi. There are several stories about them.

Today, let me tell you the story of another pair—sage Agastya and Lopamudra, who are known to have discovered the mantras.

According to the Rig Vedas, Agastya has sung many hymns. He was the teacher of both the Arya and the Dravidian tribes. He promoted harmony and a symbiotic relationship between the two.

As the story goes, once Agastya dreamt that his forefathers were hanging upside down from a tree after their death.

Aghast, he asked the reason for their predicament.

What is your idea of a family? Do you think you have any duties towards your family members?

'If you do not marry and have children,' they said, 'this will be our plight.'

So Agastya decided to marry. With his spiritual powers, he created a beautiful girl child, Lopamudra. The girl was raised by the king of Vidarbha. After she came of age, she was married off to Agastya.

Yogic practices kept Agastya always looking and feeling young. And he and Lopamudra led a happy and joyous married life.

But after a while, Agastya forgot all about Lopamudra. He went deep into the forest and began meditating. Lopamudra searched for him all over the forest. When she finally found him, she tried convincing him to settle down with her at home, in the ashram.

'Even ancient sages and yogis lived with their wives,' Lopamudra reasoned.

'Yes, my dear, you are right,' Agastya agreed.

Later, they had a son, Drdhasyu, who became a great poet and sage in his own time.

Having a family helpçs one grow mentally, emotionally and spiritually. Agastya reached great spiritual heights and we all know that; thanks to a wise wife and wonderful family.

What do you like about your family? What is an ideal family, according to you?

LET'S TALK ABOUT IT!

This story emphasises the need for a family. Can you imagine a life without yours?

Have you ever wondered why we need a family? Besides creating a lineage, a family essentially establishes a sense of belonging. It supports people with love, affection and encouragement and stands them in times of challenges. It also creates a value system, teaches life's lessons and equips individuals to deal with situations in times to come.

Most people dream of a perfect family, but perhaps there is no formula for such an ideal. It's perfectly normal to have a family with flaws. It's more about accepting what you have and working towards what works for you. Strong familial ties and families lead to a better community.

The material existence, and spiritual existence are like two wings of a bird. But we must pay attention to the guiding tail of the bird, the rudder that gives it a direction. What gives us such a direction in our life? It is the heart.

24.

Defeating the
Demon of Drought

This is the story of Vritra, who was also called the dragon or demon of drought. He captured all the waters of the world and imprisoned them in his fortresses. The earth was parched and afflicted by a severe famine. Animals and birds were dying. Plants were withering too. The gods tried to appeal to his good sense, but Vritra did not yield. The gods were afraid of him as Vritra was more powerful than all of them.

To bring an end to the gods' suffering, a new god and a warrior took birth. He was Indra, a god more powerful than Vritra. He grew up so big that he covered the heavens. Indra knew that his mission was to kill Vritra and release all the waters. He decided to act fast.

What are your goals and aspirations?

Indra visited the house of another god, Tvashtr and drank a large quantity of a magical nectar to develop courage, confidence and vigour. He also sought Lord Vishnu's help in the battle.

Lord Vishnu asked the weapon maker of the gods to create a powerful weapon for Indra. And so, the Vajra, or the thunderbolt, was made from the bones of the great rishi Dadichi, who gave up his life willingly, so that his bones could help save the world from annihilation.

Long before this war, Vritra had obtained a boon from the gods. As per the boon, he could not be killed at night or day. No weapon made from metal, wood

Have you thought of a process or path to achieve your goals?

or stone could be used to kill him. And the weapon that killed him could neither be wet nor dry. With all these conditions, the gods could not kill Vritra. But Indra had an intelligent plan.

Indra attacked Vritra in the evening, which is neither day nor night. He killed him with the Vajra, which wasn't made from wood, metal or stone but the bones of the sage Dadichi. Indra also smeared the Vajra with sea foam, which was neither wet nor dry.

The gods rejoiced. And so Indra released the waters of the world for the good of the earth and fulfilled his life's mission.

LET'S TALK ABOUT IT!

Regardless of how small or big it is, a good deed is always best done today. Indra wasted no time fulfilling his life's purpose and continued to live for many thousand years. He completed most of his duties as soon as he was born.

Even Ravana, the rakshasa king, was known to have advised Lakshmana, the younger brother of Rama, on his deathbed, 'To do good, do not delay.' Perhaps Ravana might have thought, 'If only I'd followed my wife's advice and returned Sita to Rama, my family would not have been destroyed by now.'

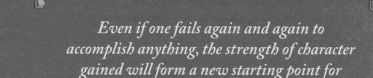

Even if one fails again and again to accomplish anything, the strength of character gained will form a new starting point for future power and triumph.
- James Allen.

25.

Brain or Brawn?

We have heard about the great wars of Mahabharata and Ramayana. But have you heard of the Battle of the Ten Kings? This ancient war finds mention in the oldest religious text of India, the Rig Veda.

Sudas and his father, King Divodasa, were good kings. They lived a life of ethics and morals. But they were surrounded by ten evil and greedy kings. Scholars and sages left the greedy kings' kingdoms and sought refuge with Divodasa and, later on, his son Sudas, who were the kings of the Bharata tribes.

Have you ever used your mind to get out of a difficult situation? How and what did you do in that case? You could make a note in your journal for future reference.

Divodasa and his army, blessed by the river goddess Saraswathi, defeated the aboriginal mountain chief Sambara Asura, and destroyed his forts. Sudas, with the guidance of Sage Vasishta, helped the Bharata tribes win the battle against the mighty army of the ten kings.

Even though the Bharata tribes were outnumbered by a larger army, Sudas won the war against the tribal alliance by

Do you have differences with your friends? What are those? How does it feel when you put aside your differences?

using strategy. He crossed the river in low tide and strategically breached a dam built between the shores. This drowned most of the enemy army that was crossing the river on foot.

Meanwhile, Guru Vasishta's prayers had secured Lord Indra's blessings. 'Let me also help the righteous side,' the King of Gods thought.

And so, Lord Indra sent out rains and floods when the kings' remaining armies were crossing the river. He also sent lightning to destroy the evil kings while King Sudas and his tiny but brave army defeated the remaining army on the banks of the River Ravi.

'Long live the King,' cried the soldiers and subjects. Everyone was jubilant.

After this victory, the war shifted to the next battleground. On the banks of the River Yamuna, the local chief Beda and his army of tribes were also defeated. Lord Indra and Sudas rewarded their allies and Guru Vasishta generously.

'Please accept these horses, cows, gold and land,' King Sudas said to all the tribal lords. This victory enabled Sudas to unite all of them and create harmony among the various chiefs.

Winning this war allowed the Bharata tribes to occupy the entire Punjab of today. The land they occupied, centred around the Saraswathi and Sindhu rivers, and became the foundation of the Bharata culture, in India, also known as Bharat. In the days of the Rig Veda, the area was known as Sapta Sindhu, or the land of seven rivers. However, the river Saraswathi disappeared over the course of time.

This story proves that victory depends not on a large army of soldiers but on strategy and divine guidance.

The Bharatas went on to sponsor the compilation of the Rig Veda in its present form. They also knew the wisdom of collaborating with their enemies, making them their friends and giving up differences.

LET'S TALK ABOUT IT!

When it comes to succeeding, the brain is more powerful than brawn. Strategies and skills are more important than the size of an army or brute force. Humility, devotion and alertness are greater than complacency and arrogance. In the Mahabharata, the Pandavas won against a larger army and stronger generals. In fact, Arjuna and Lord Krishna won against the mighty force of invincible Bhishma, Drona, Karna, Aswatthama, and Salya. Similarly, in the Bible, the little David won over the giant Goliath. With his spartan vanar sena of Hanuman, Angad and others, Lord Rama also won over the mighty giant magical Rakshasa army of Ravana. All these examples suggest that brain over brawn and the support of the divine are formulae for success.

If you put yourself at the disposal of the
divine forces, do it with conviction and love.
The objective will surely be achieved.

Heartfulness Relaxation for Children

- Sit comfortably and close your eyes, softly and gently.
- Begin with your toes. Wiggle them. Now feel them relax.
- Feel the healing energy of Mother Earth moving up into your toes, feet and ankles. Now feel it moving up your knees, relaxing the lower legs.
- Feel the healing energy moving farther up your legs. Relax your thighs.
- Now relax your hips, lower body and waist.
- Relax your back. From your tailbone to your shoulders, feel that your entire back is relaxing.
- Relax your chest and shoulders. Feel your shoulders simply melting away.
- Relax your upper arms. Relax each muscle in your forearms, your hands and right up to your fingertips.
- Relax your neck muscles.
- Take the awareness to your face. Relax your jaw, mouth, nose, eyes, earlobes, facial muscles, forehead ... all the way to the top of your head.
- Feel how your whole body is now completely relaxed. Scan your system from top to toe. If there is any part of your body that is still tense or in pain, imagine it is soaked in the healing energy of Mother Earth for a bit longer.
- When you are ready, move your attention to your heart. Rest there for a little while. Feel that you are immersed in the love and light in your heart.
- Remain still and quiet, and slowly become absorbed in yourself.
- Remain absorbed within this deep silence for as long as you want, until you feel ready to come out again.

Relaxing, isn't it?